Play Together

By Zak Belahmira   Illustrated by Mike Dammer

Target Skill Letter Recognition *Oo, Pp, Qq, Rr, Ss*
High-Frequency Words *the, little*

PEARSON
Scott
Foresman

I am Dad.

I am Dad.

I am the little cat.

I am the little dog.

I am running.

I am jumping.

Am I happy?